# WHERE'S HELLO KITTY?

First published in the UK by HarperCollins Children's Books in 2011

7 9 10 8 6

ISBN: 978-0-00-736514-2

Printed and bound in Italy

HarperCollins *Children's Books*

# How to play

Hello Kitty is super stylish! In fact, she's such a style icon that lots of girls are copying her look.

This is Mimmy, Hello Kitty's twin sister. She looks just like Hello Kitty, but she wears her bow on the other side!

It's very difficult for Mimmy to spot Hello Kitty in a crowd these days! She needs your help to find the real Hello Kitty in every scene, using the picture at the top as a guide. It's more difficult than you think; lots of girls look almost identical to Hello Kitty and just have one or two small differences.

There are lots of other fun activities inside to keep you entertained.

As well as Hello Kitty and Mimmy, you'll also find Hello Kitty's friends in each spread. Can you spot them all on every page?

**Dear Daniel**

**Thomas**

**Fifi**

**Tippy**

**Rory**

**Tim and Tammy**

**Tracy**

**Jodie**

**Moley**

**Joey**

The fairground is in town!
Help Mimmy find Hello Kitty
in the crowds before she eats
all the candyfloss herself!

Where's
Hello
Kitty?

Mimmy has arranged to meet Hello Kitty at the concert, but the room is packed full of music fans!

Where's Hello Kitty?

# Time to accessorise!

Here's your chance to style Hello Kitty. Tick the box by the accessories you would add to each fabulous outfit below!

Mimmy knows Hello Kitty is at the beach somewhere...

Where's Hello Kitty?

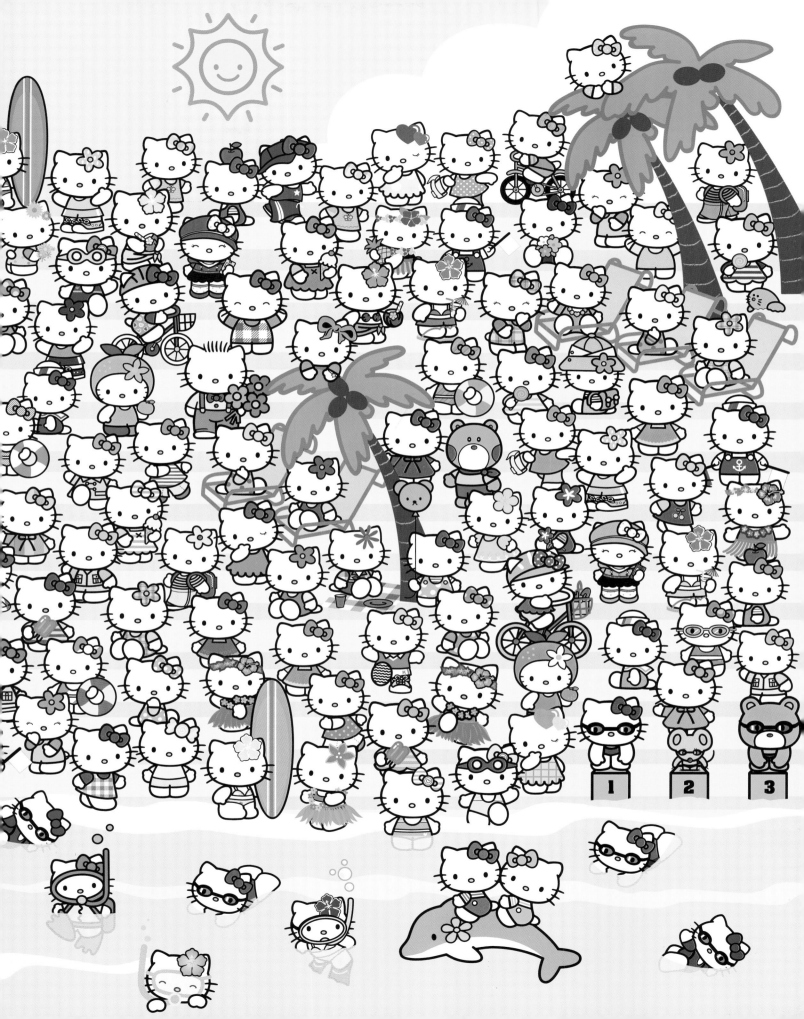

Hello Kitty has ___ pairs of shoes.

Fifi is throwing a haunted house party and has invited all of her friends!

Where's Hello Kitty?

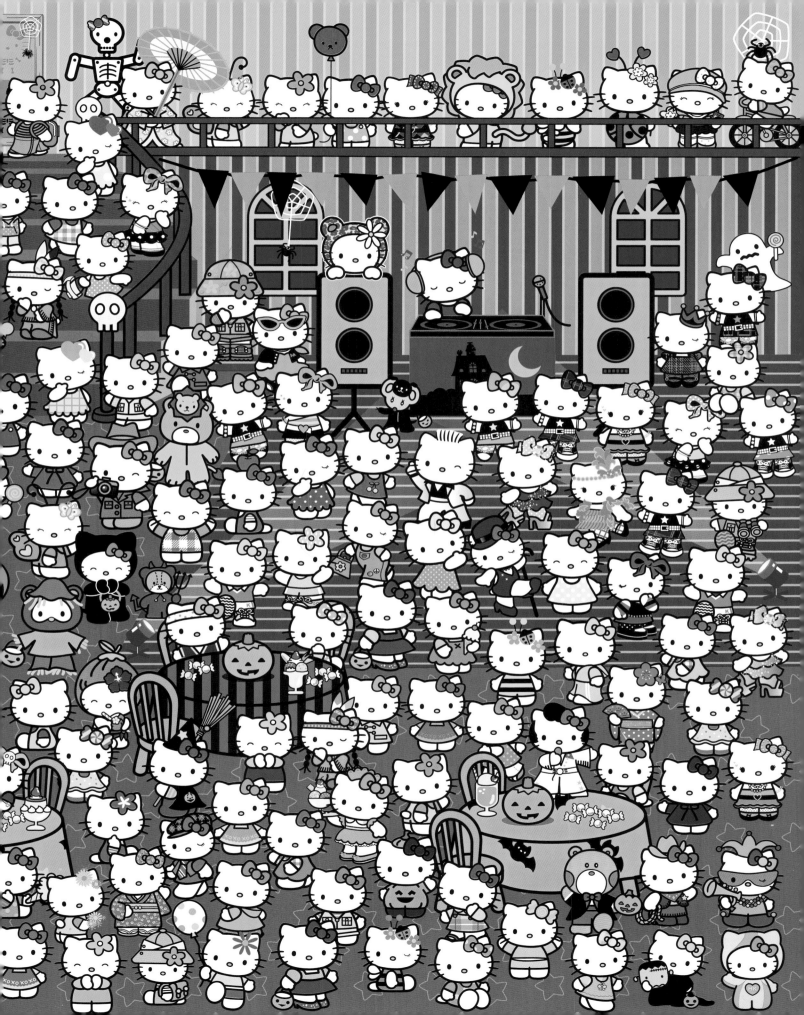

# Race to the perfect pink party dress!

**Hello Kitty is having a charity car boot sale. Beat the other Hello Kitty copycats to this beautiful dress!**

You can play this game with one or two friends. You will need: a counter each and a die.

Decide which copycat you want to be and place your counter on their starting spot. Take turns to throw the die. Whoever throws the highest number goes first, after which you take it in turns going clockwise around your group. Each player must travel once clockwise round the circle, then when they reach their starting point again, travel down the coloured path to the middle. The first person to reach the dress wins!

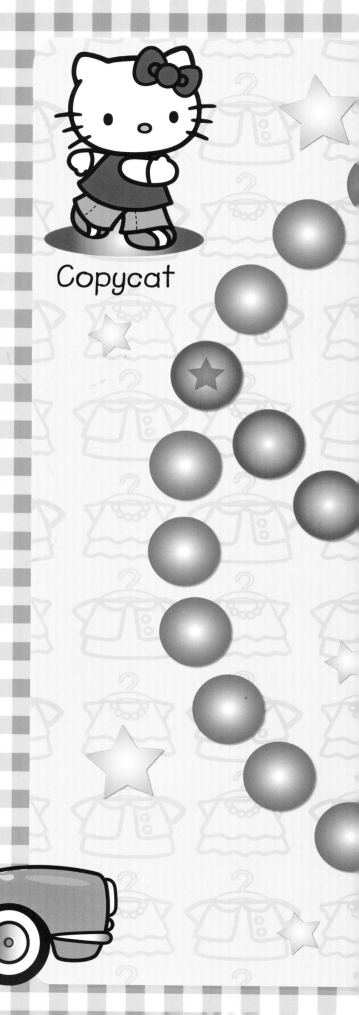

Copycat

Copycat

Copycat

It's school sports day. Hello Kitty is feeling athletic.

Where's Hello Kitty?

# How well do you know your friend?

How easily could you spot your friend in a crowd? Take this fun quiz and see how many questions you can answer correctly!

What is their favourite outfit?

What colour are their eyes?

How long is their hair?

Their hair colour is...

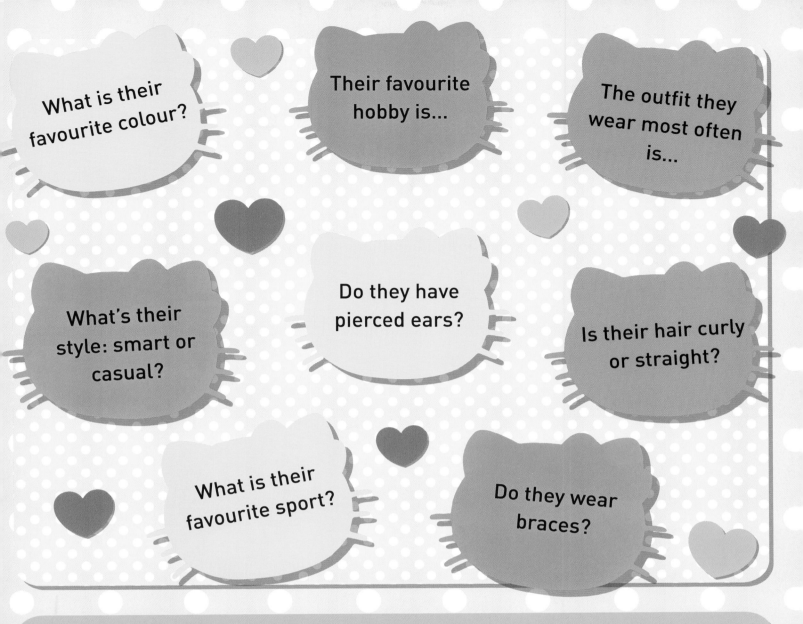

What is their favourite colour?

Their favourite hobby is...

The outfit they wear most often is...

What's their style: smart or casual?

Do they have pierced ears?

Is their hair curly or straight?

What is their favourite sport?

Do they wear braces?

# How many did you get right?

**0-4: Lots more to discover**
You need to get to know your friend better. Try organising some time together and sharing all your secrets!

**5-8: Room for improvement**
There's more to learn about your friend, so make some time for all those questions you've been dying to ask each other.

**9-12: You're best friends!**
Well done, you know your friend really well! Why not celebrate with a fun day out?

Hello Kitty and her classmates are going on a school trip. Hello Kitty was in such a hurry to get dressed this morning, she put on one red shoe and one pink shoe!

# Where's Hello Kitty?

The diner is very busy. Hello Kitty is helping to serve.

Where's Hello Kitty?

# Amazing maze!

Help Hello Kitty escape the crowd of copycats and make it back to her house! Guide her through the maze but avoid the dead ends!

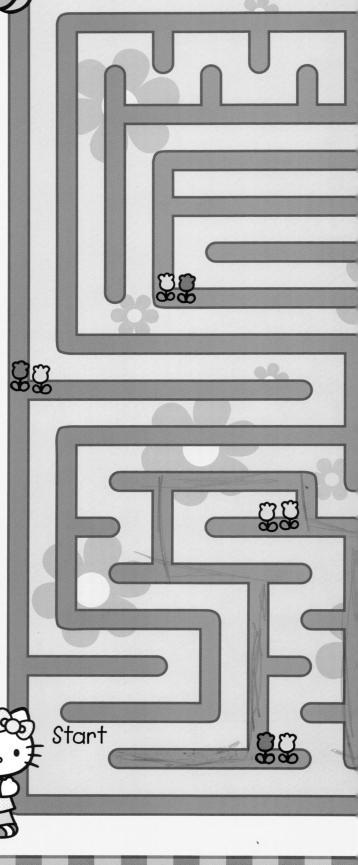

Start

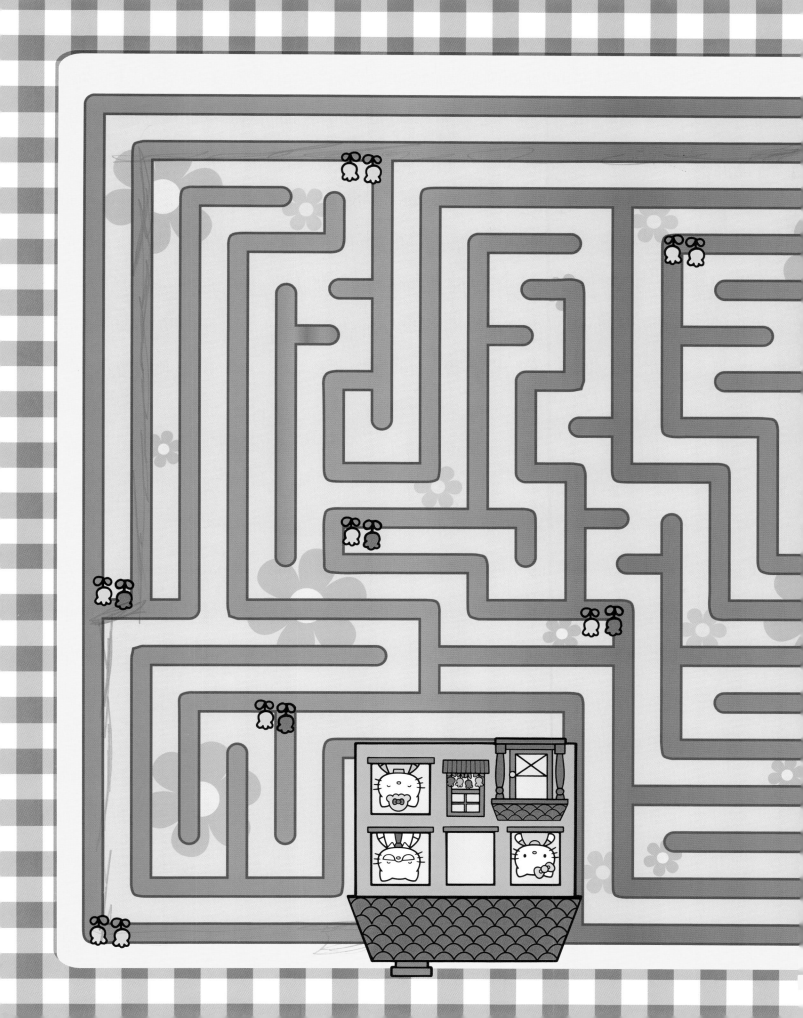

Where's Hello Kitty?

Prom night is very special, but it won't be complete without Mimmy to dance with…

A red mobile phone

A spare button
(just in case!)

A green apple
(yummy, my favourite!)

A blue envelope

A pink comb

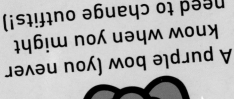

A purple bow (you never know when you might need to change outfits!)

A pair of red sunglasses

But we still need your help. I dropped my bag at the fairground! Can you help me find it? Turn back to the fairground page and search.

There's a lost item from my bag somewhere in the crowd on each of the other pages. Can you find all seven? Search all the pages until you have found every item.

Thank you for helping Mimmy find me!